Getting Ready for Football

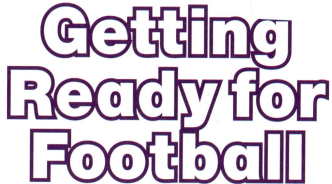

Written by Alison Hawes

Illustrated by Georgie Birkett

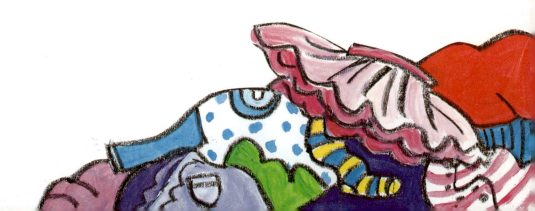

I can put on my clothes.

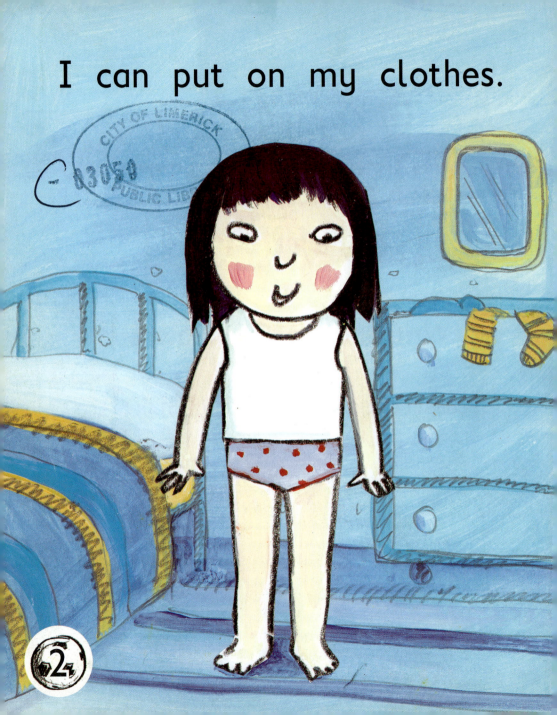

I can put on my...

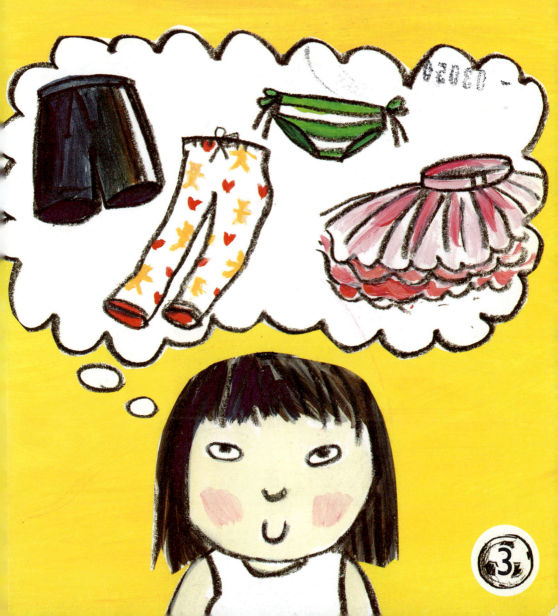

shorts.

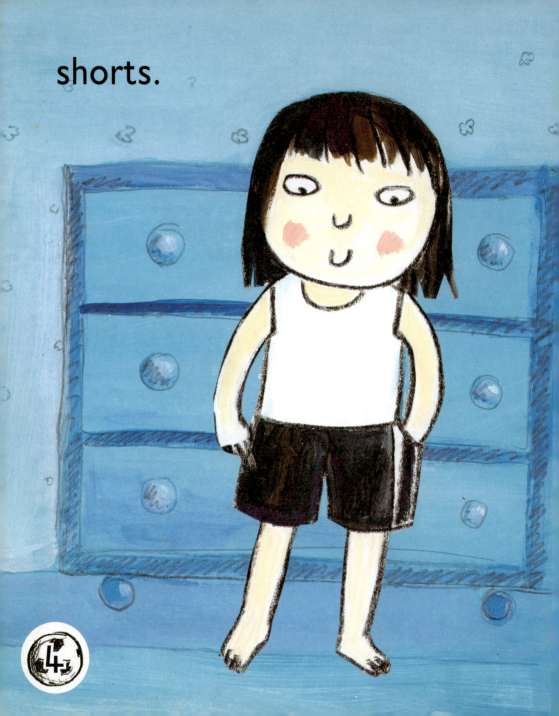

I can put on my...

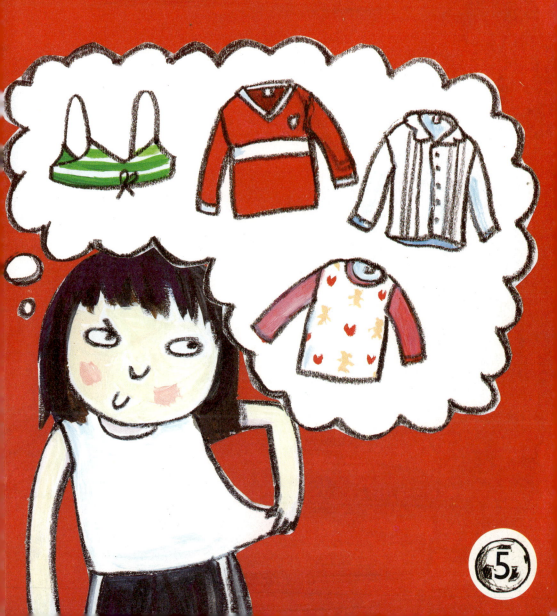

5

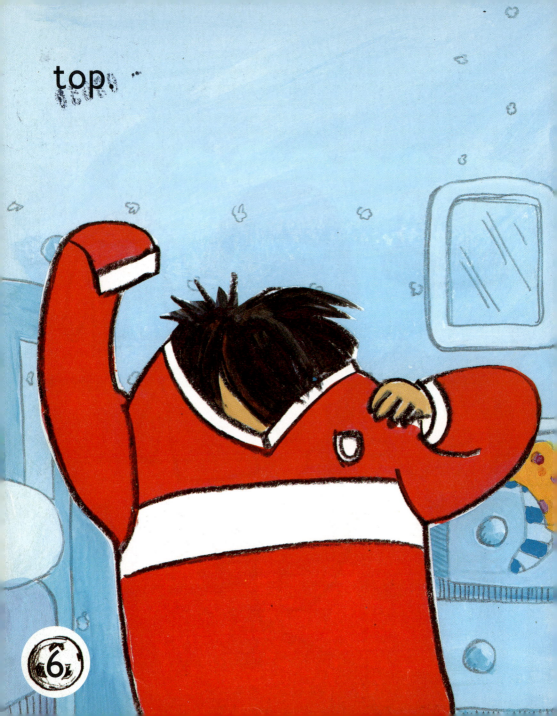

I can put on my...

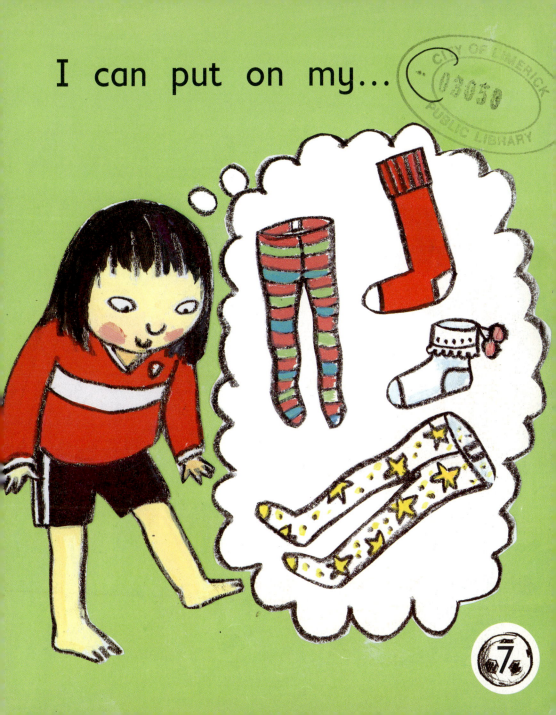

7

socks.

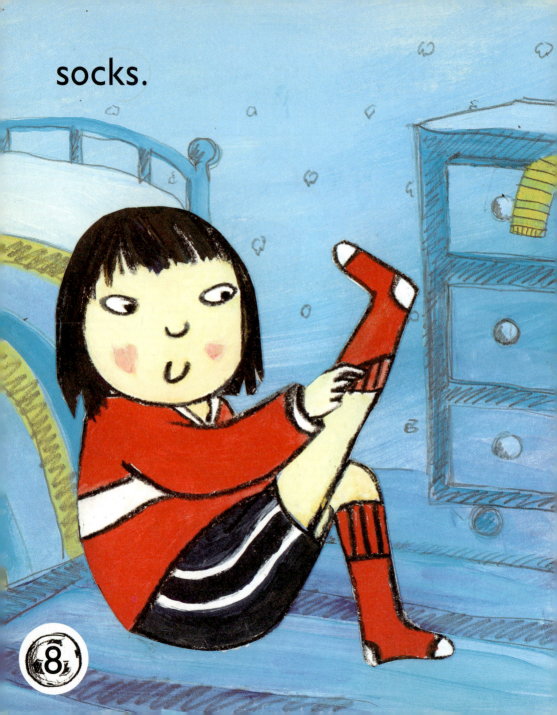

I can put on my...

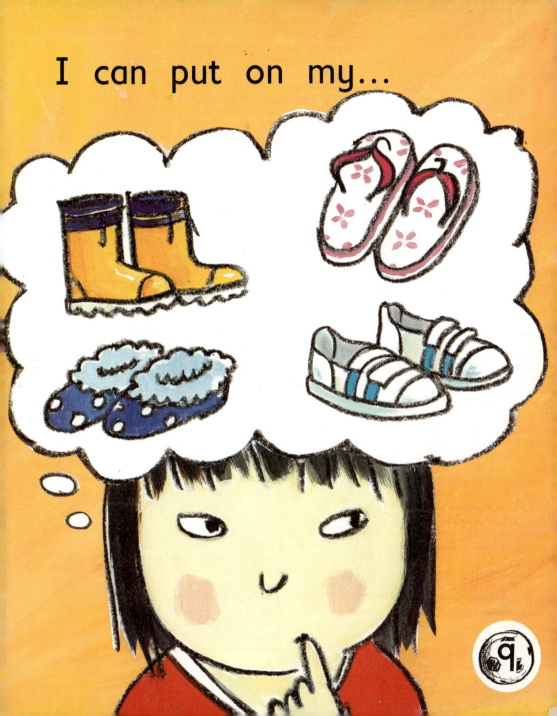

trainers.

10

Now, I can...

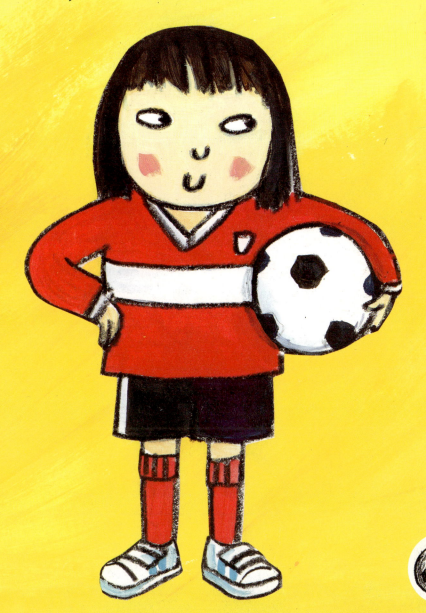

11

play football.

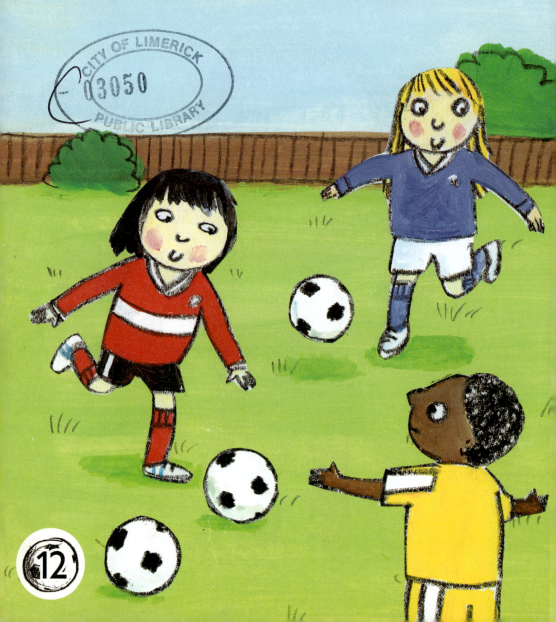

12